SRA OPEN COURT READING

School

A Division of The McGraw·Hill Companies

Columbus, Ohio

www.sra4kids.com

SRA/McGraw-Hill

A Division of The **McGraw·Hill** *Companies*

Send all inquiries to:
SRA/McGraw-Hill
8787 Orion Place
Columbus, OH 43240-4027

ISBN 0-07-569870-6
8 9 10 11 12 DBH 10 09 08 07 06

Here is the 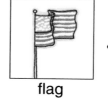 .

flag

I see the .

boys

I see the .

girls

4

I see the .

tables

I see the .

chairs

I see the  .

books

I see the  .

crayons

6

Here is the  .

teacher

Here is the .

school